The Bird THAT LIVES IN Paradise

Written by Melissa C. Marsted • **Illustrated by Cait Irwin**
Designed by Aileen Aquino

Cover and Book Design by Aileen Aquino

For inquiries or additional information, email us at melissa@luckypennypress.com,
visit our website at www.luckypennypublications.com, or
@luckypennypublications on Instagram.

ISBN 978-1-945243-48-6

"If a child is to keep alive an inborn sense of wonder, a child needs the companionship of at least one adult who can share it, rediscovering with the child the joy, excitement and mystery of the world we live in."

Rachel Carson

Welcome to Mount Rainier National Park!

I'm a red-shafted northern flicker, and my bright feathers represent fire and the new growth that comes after.

I make my home here in Mount Rainier National Park. I feel at peace when I can sit on a branch and enjoy the lovely views. Look at all of the wildflowers blooming: lupine, Queen Anne's lace, and asters. I am mesmerized by their colors: colors of happiness, joy, and most of all love.

But many of my animal friends are in danger. The scary effects of climate change are closing in all around us. I must begin my flight to warn my fellow animals that live in this lovely state of Washington.

I sense some quivering beneath the earth's surface. I must act quickly before it's too late!

Time to follow the Wonderland Trail that circles Mount Rainier, the highest peak in the Cascade Range.

Watch me soar! I'll catch some yummy insects before I make my way to Mount St. Helens.

Look at all of the monarch butterflies. They drink nectar from wildflowers so they have the energy to make the long migration to Mexico.

Along my way, I'll occasionally drop a feather as a message to the animals that I am watching out for signs of danger. It's my job to warn the animals about our warming planet.

Mount Rainier has 26 glaciers. A glacier is formed when snow stays in one place year after year and becomes ice. During the dry summer months, a slow melt provides water for nearby rivers.

Let's take a look at Emmons Glacier, one of the largest in North America. Nowadays, it is melting more and more in the warmer spring and fall months than in past years. The water flowing into the local rivers is too warm, making it harder for trout and salmon to survive.

Let's fly over the top of Mount Rainier so you can see my view: a bird's eye view!

Did you know that Mount Rainier is a stratovolcano? That means it is made up of layers of lava and ash that formed over many years. This volcano is resting peacefully...for now.

When the animals are not kind to each other, the volcano might decide it's time to show its anger! We must all be kind!

Mount Rainier National Park is my home. It is where I feel safe, but I must take flight and explore the state before it's too late. My animal friends need my help.

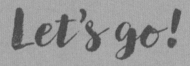

Let's go!

It's time to check out Mount St. Helens National Volcanic Monument and see how the animals are doing on this hot day.

Many years ago, the indigenous native Americans named the volcano Loowit or Louwala-Clough, which meant "smoking mountain." She represented peace between Mount Adams and Mount Hood. The people cherished her beauty. They knew her dangers. Loowit reminded them to treat all of the forests, mountains, and animals with respect. She warned them with her grumbling and her steam. The people followed these warnings, so there was peace in nature for a very long time.

I'm leaving this feather to let my friends know that I have been here.

MOUNT ST. HELENS

. . . .

Like Mount Rainier, Mount St. Helens is also a stratovolcano. The red hot magma boils below the surface of the earth. One day, it shoots up through the volcano. A cloud of ash and rocks spews high over the top of Mount St. Helens, and the magma blows up into the air. The lava eventually settles and cools. This is how the layers are formed.

The volcano warns us that we are not being kind to others in nature.

Kindness matters!

Nowadays, small mammals called pikas make their homes in the lava fields. Pikas are herbivores, which means they eat plants. They spend the short summers collecting all of the food they'll need for winter, and they particularly like to munch on the fireweed that grows where the lava flowed down the side of the volcano.

But today, the warmer summers and thinner snowpack are a bigger threat to pikas than the volcano. They can't take the heat, and if they don't gather enough food, they might not make it to spring. They need our help!

I hear some grumbling. Look at the steam rising into the sky!

Mount St. Helens is very grand, but it is too scary for me to live here. Mount Rainier is where I find my paradise, but I will keep traveling to see how things are going at two of the other national parks in Washington.

Off to Olympic National Park!

Follow me!

OLYMPIC
National Park

• • • • • • • • • •

There's a lot to explore at Crescent Lake and Maymere Falls. I see some Olympic marmots. They are endemic to this national park, which means they are found here and nowhere else. The mountain meadows are perfect places for them to call home. They love to chase each other through the grasses and hide in their burrows!

The marmots must always be on the lookout. There are many dangers, such as the coyotes that lurk in the shadows and the warming temperatures that are making it harder for marmots to survive.

Off to the next stop.

The Pacific Ocean!

Ahhh...I love how the breeze feels as it ripples through my feathers! And look what I see in the ocean: a couple of gray whales.

They were an endangered species at one time, but now they are protected. They look so graceful swimming in the waves.

Watch this! I'm going to fly onto the back of one of the whales. How cool! I can feel the waves on my feet, but it's time to keep going. I'll meet some other animals.

HOH RAIN FOREST

• • • • • • • • • • •

I've arrived at the Hoh Rain Forest. It's a little too dark and spooky for me. And it's so tiring to weave through the towering trees and dense canopy.

Here it rains 140 inches each year! When it's not raining, it's often very foggy. The forest has the perfect conditions for the moss and ferns.

See what I found! It's called a banana slug, the second biggest slug in the world. It can grow up to 10 inches.

It looks tasty, but I'll let this slug meander over the lush moss. I can find something to eat at my next stop!

I've seen some big trees in my life, but none like the ones in Olympic National Park. Some of the world's largest spruce trees can be found here.

It's a long way to North Cascades National Park. Mother Nature has been warning me and many of my animal friends. I've heard rumors of scary wildfires near North Cascades.

I see a goldfinch perched on a branch over there. Maybe this little finch will join me, so we can check out the wildfires together. We can protect and help each other.

Off we go, but we must be careful.

NORTH CASCADES
National Park

· · · · · · · · ·

This is not paradise! This is a disaster!

Oh no! Look at the flames. I see smoke, too! That must be the Cedar Creek Fire.

This smoke is terrible. My lungs hurt so much. We have to keep going. We need to check on our friends and make sure they are safe. We must! We must!

We can follow the Skagit River to head deeper into the park. We're almost there! Can you see those majestic peaks in the distance?

Quick! Let's follow the deer. And the owl and pine marten! They seem to know where they're going. They'll help us escape the flames!

They must be heading to Diablo Lake. We'll be safe if we can make it there.

DIABLO LAKE VISTA POINT

· · · · · · · · · ·

Ahhh....fresh air...finally, we can breathe again.
That smoke was so thick. It's a relief to be out of
harm's way.

I've heard about this spot many times. It's very
beautiful, but I don't want to live here. The fire
danger is too scary for me. The temperatures are
rising, and the glaciers in the park are getting
smaller and smaller. The view is incredible, and it's
so peaceful, but it is too risky for me.

"What do you think, little finch?"

"Is this your paradise?"

"It looks like you have found your happy place. You look lovely surrounded by those rhododendron blossoms. I'm glad that you have reunited with your family and friends. They must have been so worried. Take care of them, especially the little ones. It is time for me to continue on my journey."

"Bye for now!"

I've finished my tour of this great state of Washington. My wings are tired, and my heart is heavy from the threats my animal friends are facing. But I'm relieved to head back home.

I will drop a few more feathers along the way to Mount Rainier to remind the other animals that I have passed over them. They will know I care about their safety.

Maybe, just maybe, spreading my feathers will inspire humans to protect the environment and the habitats that my animal friends call home.

With so many dangers, I will do my best to help them.

For now, Mount Rainier National Park is my home.
It is my paradise.

Come visit me sometime and see what you think.
Where is your paradise? Wherever it may be,
remember to be nice to nature and wildlife.

My animal friends will return your kindness with awe,
beauty, and love!

Until next time!

Wildlife Adventures for Young Readers

Buzzy and the Redrock Canyons
WRITTEN BY MELISSA C. MARSTED AND ILLUSTRATED BY IZZY GREER

Buzzy the bee zips across the state of Utah introducing readers to Utah's five national parks, starting with Arches, then continuing to Canyonlands, and finally crossing the state to Capitol Reef, Bryce Canyon, and Zion National Parks. Buzzy teaches readers about animals and endangered species that live in the parks as well as how arches, hoodoos, and spires were formed many years ago. *Buzzy and the Red Rock Canyons* is a great introduction to the wonders and magic of nature and the national parks system, originally established over 100 years ago.

Casey Cruises California
WRITTEN BY MELISSA C. MARSTED AND ILLUSTRATED BY IZZY GREER

Readers join Casey, a California quail, on a journey through the nine national parks in his beautiful home state. Casey starts the adventure in the north at Redwoods National Park and narrates his way southward through forests with massive trees, majestic glacial formations, searing deserts, and sublime Pacific Islands, finally returning to the north to end his travels at Pinnacles National Park, and the Golden Gate Bridge, the world's gateway to California. Along the way Casey meets a variety of animal friends who help him understand the unique qualities of each park, and he also teaches readers some of the history and amazing fun facts about the parks.

Tiny's Grand Adventure
WRITTEN BY MELISSA C. MARSTED AND ILLUSTRATED BY RUTHANNE HAMRICK

Join Tiny, a black-chinned hummingbird, as he travels across the American Southwest visiting eight national parks in Nevada, Arizona, New Mexico and Texas. Tiny meets many animal friends along the way; these friendships show us all that the differences between them are at the heart of the wonder of nature. It's a long journey for this little hummingbird, but as Tiny flies freely from place to place without borders or walls, he is proof positive that even the smallest of us can do big things.

The Secret Life of Phil
WRITTEN BY MELISSA C. MARSTED AND ILLUSTRATED BY CAIT IRWIN

The Secret Life of Phil explores the Black Hills of Wyoming and South Dakota through the journey of an endangered black-footed ferret. Phil encounters other endangered species and hides from predators in awe-inspiring places like Badlands National Park, Devils Tower National Monument, and Mount Rushmore National Memorial. The black-footed ferret is protected by the Endangered Species Act. Our story aims to raise awareness among our readers about endangered species and the important role we all play in protecting them. Most of all, *The Secret Life of Phil* seeks to inspire a sense of wonder about the beauty and magic of nature.

Molly's Tale of the American Pikas
WRITTEN BY MELISSA C. MARSTED AND ILLUSTRATED BY RUTHANNE HAMRICK

Molly the Meadowlark takes readers on a journey through five national parks that are currently threatened by climate change. Molly introduces us to the pika, an adorable mammal that can be found in each of the national parks Molly visits. Molly teaches young readers about pikas, including how they escape from other animals who hunt them. But what is an even greater danger to our pikas than all of these predators? Read *Molly's Tale of the American Pikas* to learn more about how changes in weather and climate are some of the biggest threats to the pika's way of life.

Sadie's Search for Truth and Beauty
WRITTEN BY MELISSA C. MARSTED AND ILLUSTRATED BY LYNETTE NICHOLS

Join Sadie, a greater sage-grouse, as she takes her three chicks throughout the Colorado Plateau and tells them stories about the ancient ruins and the magnificent rock formations that they encounter along the way. Sadie protects her chicks from the desert predators and teaches them how to search for water. On their journey, Sadie will reveal secrets to her chicks passed down by the Ancestral Puebloans. The chicks will learn survival skills. Will they find enough water to mature into adults? Open the pages filled with magical illustrations to learn more about the desert southwest.

Wildlife Adventures for Young Readers, continued

DeeDee's Year of Adventure
WRITTEN BY MELISSA C. MARSTED AND ILLUSTRATED BY CAIT IRWIN

Join DeeDee, a black-capped chickadee, as she begins her life learning to fly from her nest at the end of the spring. Her journey over, above and all around Acadia National Park, the only National Park in all of New England, takes her through the four seasons as she meets different animals along the way including a great blue heron, peregrine falcons, sand birds, a lobster, otters, a moose, a snowy owl and more. DeeDee knows she is in for a fluffy, white surprise, but only time will reveal the ultimate joy when she experiences what this means.

Hope Soars Over Yellowstone
WRITTEN BY MELISSA C. MARSTED AND ILLUSTRATED BY CAIT IRWIN

Follow Hope, a bald eagle who lost her favorite tree during a lightning storm. She flies over all of Yellowstone National Park looking for a new tree to call home. As Hope soars with the wind currents, she meets some of the mammals that reside in Yellowstone. Readers will enjoy accompanying Hope as she glides throughout one of our country's most impressive national parks and seeks a safe, new home. Follow her and find where she decides to land.

COMING SOON

Olé's Dark Sky Journey
WRITTEN BY MELISSA C. MARSTED AND ILLUSTRATED BY VICKI SPECK

For our newest book in our Wildlife Adventures for Young Readers series, Olé, an endangered Mexican spotted owl, begins his dark sky journey at Mesa Arch in Canyonlands NP. He observes a new constellation at each stop as he makes his way around the state of Utah, with one quick stop at Great Basin National Park in Nevada. The eight phases of the moon will also guide Olé along the way. Come along and enjoy where he soars through the dark, dark skies.

About the Designer

photo credit:
Jamie Lewis

Aileen Aquino graduated with a BS in Visual Communication Design from The Ohio State University. She has been working at various design firms, architectural firms, and contemporary art museums for close to 20 years. Aileen specializes in print design and, in her free time, creates pieces for her own letterpress company in Salt Lake City. She enjoys exploring the outdoors with her two children – whether it's skiing, hiking, mountain biking, or climbing – and reveling in their awe of the world around them. She is passionate about designing books she can share with her children, who have inherited her love of books, art, and travel.

About the Illustrator

photo credit:
Julie Buckles

Cait Irwin is a professional artist as well as a published author, activist, entrepreneur, naturalist, and world traveler. Being an artist and having a deep connection with the natural world are two major constants in her life. Her artwork spans a wide spectrum of media, styles, and subject matter.

A native of South Dakota, Cait graduated from Northland College in Wisconsin in 2003 with a BA in Studio Art with an emphasis in environmental studies. She stayed in the Northwoods area for several years, during which time she created murals, wrote a book, and taught herself woodworking. Cait eventually moved to Council Bluffs, Iowa to be closer to family and become a full-time artist. Seven years ago, she founded Irwin Artworks, LLC.

To learn more about Cait, visit her website *www.irwinartworks.com*. Her artwork is also available for purchase at *www.etsy.com/shop/irwinartworks*.

About Lucky Penny Publications

Dear Readers –

For as long as I can remember, I have loved to write, and I especially like to write letters. I've decided to include a letter with each book in our series to offer background as to how I decided on Washington state and the flicker as our narrator, how I came up with the title, and how I chose which animals to represent. My second grade teacher at Cherry Brook Elementary School in Canton, Connecticut, inspired my creativity and imagination many years ago. I began writing children's books in 2002 when my own two sons were in elementary school. I started writing the Wildlife Adventures for Young Readers series in 2016.

My maternal grandfather, a landscape architect, and my grandmother, an artist, introduced me to the love of adventure, nature, and birds during my childhood. More than 50 years ago, the Roaring Brook Nature Center offered nature and bird walks where we learned about indigo buntings and cedar wax wings.

As I watched my suet feeder in 2021, I had two majestic flickers that came regularly. Their presence offered hope during the months and months of the Covid pandemic. As soon as I made the decision to use the flicker as our primary narrator, I saw them everywhere!

Once this book began to blossom, I knew it was time to get on the road. I could tie in the research with the 2021 Vacation Races Mount Rainier Half Marathon. Three national parks plus Mount St. Helens became the basis for this story. On the second day of our journey, the road through North Cascades National Park was closed due to three wildfires. We had to skip North Cascades and went directly to Olympic National Park, following the same circular route as the flicker in this story.

I had visited Mount Rainier in August of 2008, so I was already familiar with Paradise Valley, which prompted the idea for the title to tie into my great grandfather AC Gilbert's autobiography, *The Man Who Lives in Paradise*, published in 1954.

For me, a soaring bird symbolizes freedom and serenity. With life's trials and tribulations, nature never disappoints and almost always inspires. That is my hope, too - that our books are fun, educational, and inspirational. The more you notice, the more nature will send you messages. Nature is everywhere for all of us to enjoy.

Happy Reading,

Melissa Marsted

About the Author

photo credit:
Maeve Lawlor

Melissa grew up in a small town in northwestern Connecticut where she built forts in the woods and picked wild raspberries. Her second grade teacher inspired her lifelong love of writing. After losing her house in the Santa Barbara Tea Fire in 2008, she self-published her first children's book and started Lucky Penny Publications. She relocated to Utah in 2013 and began writing children's books about the national parks in 2016. An avid long-distance runner, Melissa creates her books by running along the same trails as the animals she writes about in her books. Melissa now has Clover, a vizsla born on a farm in northern Utah, to accompany her on their road trips. Melissa believes that being in nature is where the magic of synchronicity and creativity happens. Instagram @*luckypennypublications*.

"Hold fast to dreams, for if dreams die, life is a broken-winged bird that cannot fly."

Langston Hughes

Marymere Falls, Olympic National Park │ photo credit: **Melissa Marsted**

Fun Facts

- *The Bird That Lives in Paradise* represents the ninth book in our Wildlife Adventures for Young Readers series. The research took place during the summer of 2021. There were three fires burning in North Cascades National Park at the time.

- The title is inspired by both the book written by the author's great grandfather, *The Man Who Lives in Paradise*, and the Paradise area on the south side of Mount Rainier, which includes Paradise Valley, Paradise Glacier, and the beginning of the Paradise River.

- Mount Rainier last erupted in 1894. Soon after, it was designated the fifth national park in the country, even before the National Park Service was established in 1916.

- Mount Rainier is the tallest peak in the Cascade Range that extends from Canada through Washington, Oregon, and into Northern California.

- The flicker follows our research journey around Olympic National Park in 2021.

- President Franklin Delano Roosevelt visited the Olympic Peninsula in 1937, and the following year, he signed an act designating Olympic National Park.

- North Cascades National Park was established by President Lyndon B. Johnson in 1968.

- The North Cascades are sometimes called the American Alps, and at roughly 9,200', Goode Mountain is the tallest peak in the national park.

- At one time, 750 glaciers were recorded in North Cascades National Park, but with the changing climate, there now remain just over 300. The glaciers make up about ⅓ of all the glaciers in the United States (excluding Alaska), but since the late 1880s, more than 50% of the ice and snow regions have melted.

- Many animals are endangered within North Cascades National Park including peregrine falcons, gray wolves, grizzly bears, and northern spotted owls.

- Bald eagles in the Pacific Northwest eat a variety of prey, but their primary food source is fish such as salmon. The Skagit River is the only river in Washington that is home to all five species of Pacific salmon: Chinook (king), chum (dog), Coho (silver), pink (humpy), and sockeye (red).

- The ash-black slug is the world's largest slug species. Most ash-black slugs are 4-8 inches long, but some can grow up to 12 inches.

For more information about Wildlife Adventures for Young Readers or Lucky Penny Publications, please email us at *melissa@luckypennypress.com*. For updates on our newest books, please click on our website www.luckypennypublications.com or our Instagram @luckypennypublications.

Things You Can Do with Your Family and Friends to Help Wildlife, Plants and Our Environment

1. When using public trails that allow dogs, always keep your dog on a leash. Being chased stresses all animals. They already have plenty of natural predators to worry.

2. Wildfires can destroy the homes and food supplies of wildlife. If you go camping, never leave your campfire unattended, and make sure to put your fire all the way out.

3. Reduce waste, resist using single-use plastic water bottles and plastic bags and bring reusable bags with you when shopping.

4. Recycle everything you can, especially plastic water bottles, aluminum cans, glass bottles, and paper products.

5. Consider finding a place outside to start a compost bin for all of your apple cores, banana peels, orange rinds, and vegetable trimmings.

6. Whenever you are in a car, ask the driver to avoid idling by turning off the car while waiting at the bank or other drive-throughs.

7. When you are taking a shower or a bath or brushing your teeth, think about the amount of water you use and try to limit your use of water.

8. Remember to turn off the lights when you leave a room. Also, unplug the chargers to your electronic devices when they are fully charged.

9. Volunteer for trash and litter clean-ups in your neighborhood. Volunteer at a community garden. Plant bee and hummingbird friendly plants in your backyard.

10. Finally, get out in nature! Take a hike. Go on a run. Breathe fresh air. See if you can identify the plants, birds, and anything else you see or hear in nature.

If you do just a few of these things, you'll set a great example of what it means to care for our environment.

Made in the USA
Middletown, DE
15 April 2023

28897651R00029